All Creatures   (A)

Be kind to one another and to every living thing
Be kind to all the animals and birds upon the wing
Be kind to all the fishes that are swimming in the sea
Be kind to every living thing, they're just like you and me.

The Ostrich   (B)

Here is the ostrich straight and tall   *(stretch arm*
Nodding his head above us all.   *above head)*
Here is the hedgehog prickly and small   *(hands together,*
Rolling himself into a ball.   *fingers sticking out)*
Here is the snake on the ground
Wriggling among the stones he's found.
Here is the spider scuttling round
Treading so lightly on the ground.
Here are the birds that fly so high
Spreading their wings across the sky.
Here are the children fast asleep   *(head on hands)*
And in the night the owls do peep   *(fingers ring*
Tu whit, tu whoo, tu whit, tu whoo   *round eyes)*

Frogs Jump

Frogs jump
Caterpillars hump
Worms wiggle
Bugs jiggle
Rabbits hop
Horses gallop
Snakes slide
Seagulls glide
Mice creep
Deer leap
Puppies bounce
Kittens pounce
Lions stalk
But I walk.

The Farm   (S)

I went to visit a farm one day
And saw a . . . . . . across the way
And this is what I heard them say . . . .

*(With each repetition, put in a different animal
and make the appropriate noise for the last word)*

My Pigeons

My pigeon's house I open wide
To set all my pigeons free.
They fly about on every side
And perch on the highest tree.
And when they return from their merry, merry flight
They close their eyes and say goodnight.
Coo-oo   Coo-oo   Coo-oo   Coo-oo
Coo-oo   Coo-oo   Goodnight.

Run Little Chicken

Run little chicken, run, run, run,
Run around the haystack, run, run, run,
Run around the farmyard, run, run, run,
Now back to Mother Hen quickly, run, run, run.

1

A Little Rabbit (H)

A little rabbit on a hill *(two fingers*
Was bobbing up and down *sticking up)*
His little tail was soft and white *(fist clenched)*
His two long ears were brown. *(two fingers)*
But when he heard a tiny noise *(point to ears)*
His eyes were black as coal *(point to eyes)*
His little whiskers trembled
And he scuttled down a hole. *(hand behind back)*

Mr. Cock and Mrs. Hen (G)

"Hello" said Mr. Cock, "Good Day" said Mrs. Hen
"Come and see my family, in all they number ten".
Then ten little chicks came, some white, some yellow too,
But Mr. Cock, his head held high, said
"Cock a doodle doo".

Robin Redbreast (A)

Little Robin Redbreast
Sat upon a rail
Niddle noddle went his head
And waggle went his tail
Niddle noddle went his head
And waggle went his tail
As little Robin Redbreast
Sat upon a rail.

The Spider

Big black spider
Climbing up the wall
Never, never, never
Seems to fall.
Yet I always fall
When I climb the garden gate,
I've only got two legs
And he's got eight.

The Elephant (C)

An elephant went out one day
Upon a piece of string to play.
He thought it such a jolly stunt
That he called another elephant.
Two elephants went out one day (etc)
. . . .
All of a sudden the string broke
And down came all the elephant folk.

The Mouse (A)

There's such a tiny little mouse
Living safely in my house.
Out at night he'll softly creep
When everyone is fast asleep.
But always in the light of day
He'll softly, softly creep away.
But always in the light of day
He'll softly, softly creep away.

2

An Elephant (D)

An Elephant walks like this and that,
He's terribly tall and terribly fat.
He has no fingers
He has no toes.
But goodness gracious, what a nose.

Elephant (C)

The elephant is big and strong
His ears are large, his trunk is long
He walks around with heavy tread
His keeper walking at his head.

The Dancing Elephant (B)

If you should meet an elephant
Upon a Summers day
What would you do?
What would you say?
I'd say Good Morning Elephant
And how do you do
I'd say Good Morning Elephant
And may I dance with you.

The Owl (E)

There's a big eyed owl
With a pointed nose
Two pointed ears
And claws for his toes.
He sits in a tree
And looks at you
And flaps his wings
And cries Whoo-hoo.

The Duckling (A)

I think it was the best of luck
That I was born a little duck
With yellow socks and yellow shoes
So I may wander where I choose.

Robin (B)

When father takes his spade to dig
Then Robin comes along.
He sits upon a little twig.
And sings a little song.

Or, if the trees are rather far
He does not stay alone
But comes up close to where we are
And bobs upon a stone.

Incy Wincy Spider (S)

Incy Wincy Spider climbed up the spout
Down came the rain and washed the spider out
Out came the sun and dried up all the rain
So Incy Wincy Spider climbed up that spout again.

The Tortoise (C)

The Tortoise can't go out to play
Or sell his house or rent it
For when he moves his house moves too
And nothing can prevent it.

Wiggly Woo (S)

There's a worm at the bottom of the garden
And his name is wiggly woo
There's a worm at the bottom of the garden
And all that he can do
Is to wiggle all night
And wiggle all day
Whatever else the folk may say.
There's a worm at the bottom of the garden
And his name is wiggly,
Wig Wig Wiggly
Wig wig wiggly woo oo oo, woo oo oo.

Holidays (L)

When we have a holiday
Oh what shall we do?
We'll take a little bus ride and go to the zoo.
We like the monkeys best of all,
We like the way they jump.
They climb up high with hands and feet,
and sometimes slide down bump.

The Elephant is big and strong
Just watch what he can do
He'll take a penny in his trunk
And ring a bell for you.

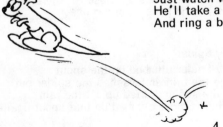

The kangaroos stand very still
Just looking all around.
Then suddenly away they go
All leaping off the ground.

4

Peter Rabbit (F)

Peter Rabbit has a fly upon his nose
Peter Rabbit has a fly upon his nose
Peter Rabbit has a fly upon his nose
So he flicked and he flicked and the fly flew away.
Powder puffs and curly whiskers
Powder puffs and curly whiskers
Powder puffs and curly whiskers
So he flicked and he flicked and the fly flew away.

Mrs. Pigeon (F)

Mrs. Peck Pigeon went picking for bread
Bob, bob, bob goes her little round head.
Tame as a pussy cat in the street
Step step step go her little red feet.
With her little red feet and her little round head
Mrs. Peck Pigeon goes picking for bread.

All Around the House (E)

One little mouse wakes up from sleep
One little mouse goes creep, creep, creep
One little mouse cries squeak, squeak, squeak
All around the house.

Two little mice wake up from sleep
. . . . (up to 5)

My Pony (C)

I have a little pony, I feed him oats and hay.
I open up the stable door to let him out to play.
He gallops here, he gallops there,
Galloping, galloping everywhere.
Never stopping till I call
Whoa my pony --- Whoa!

My Donkey (E)

If I had a donkey and he wouldn't go
Do you think I'd beat him? Oh no no no,
I'd put him in a stable and keep him nice and warm.
The best little donkey that ever was born.

Mrs. Snail

Mrs. Snail . . . . . Mrs. Snail
You leave a lovely silver trail
So we can see where you have been
S - L - O - W Mrs. Snail
(to be said very slowly)

5

Mousie

Mousie came a creeping
*(Close one fist & push the first finger
 of the other hand slowly through)*
A peeping - peeping *(waggle finger)*
Mousie said I'd like to stay
But I haven't time today.
Mousie popped into his hole
(Draw finger back quickly)
And said Achoo-Achoo
I've got a cold. *(Sneeze)*

Grandma & Granddad   (E)

Here are grandma's spectacles
Here is grandma's hat
This is the way she folds her hands
And puts them in her lap.

Here are granddads glasses
Here is granddads hat
This is the way he folds his arms
And takes a little nap.

Little Partner   (N)

Little partner take my hand
And run across the golden sand.
Climb upon the rock with me,
Then dive into the deep blue sea.
Swim around the rowing boat,
Then lying on our backs, we'll float
Turn around and swim once more,
Until we reach the sandy shore.

The Caterpillar

Who's that tickling my back said the wall.
It's me, said the caterpillar,
I'm learning to crawl.

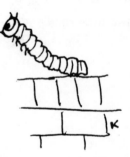

Mrs. Polly   (S)

Mrs Polly had a dolly who was sick sick sick
So she phoned for the doctor to come quick quick quick.
The doctor came with his bag and his hat
And he knocked at the door with a rat-a-tat tat.
He looked at the dolly and he shook his head
And he said 'Mrs Polly, put her straight to bed'.
He wrote on the paper for a pill pill pill
"I'll be back in the morning with the bill bill bill".

Little Brown Mouse   (E)

Behind our big cupboard right down on the floor
Lived a little brown mouse with a hole for the door.
I saw him just once, then he scampered away,
I wish he had stayed with me just for a day.

The Night Owl (A)

A big brown owl lives in a tree
In a hole in the hollow tree.
Listen to what he said to me:
Tu-whit, tu-whoo!

"At night I fly across the sky,
If you listen you'll hear my cry,
Tu-whit, tu-whoo, tu-whit, tu-whoo.

Across the fields and wood I roam
To catch my supper and take it home,
Tu-whit, tu-whoo, tu-whit, tu-whoo.

But when the sky is bright with sun
Flying back to my hole I come,
Tu-whit, tu-whoo, tu-whit, tu-whoo.

And when the sparrows start to cheep
I close my eyes and (Yawn) go - to - sleep.
(softly) Tu-whit, tu-whoo, tu-whit, tu-whoo.

Arabella Miller (Q)

Little Arabella Miller found a woolly caterpillar
First it crawled upon her mother
Then upon her baby brother.
They all said "Arabella Miller,
Take away that caterpillar."

There's a Sandy Girl (S)

There's a Sandy girl sitting on a stone
Crying, weeping, all the day alone.

Get up Sandy girl
Wipe your tears away
Choose the one you love the best
And then run away.

A Little Mouse (C)

A little mouse lived in a hole
Down by the kitchen door
The mouse came out to look for crumbs
All on the kitchen floor.
As he was nibbling this and that
Out jumped a big fat pussy cat.
Then off ran mousie to his hole
Down by the kitchen door.

Billy Bumble (C)

Hurrah for Billy Bumble
Who had a big tumble
Up he jumped
And rubbed his bump
And didn't even grumble.

The Beehive (D)

Here is the beehive, where are the bees?
Hiding inside where nobody sees.
Here they come now out of the hive.
One, two, three, four, five.

Tommy and Jo (P)

A straight back has Tommy
A straight back has Jo.
2 arms has Tommy
2 arms has Jo.
2 legs has Timmy
2 legs has Jo
A round face has Tommy
A round face has Jo.
Two eyes has Tommy
Two eyes has Jo.
A straight nose has Tommy
A straight nose has Jo
But a smiling mouth has Tommy
And a cross mouth has Jo.
And we do like Tommy
But we're sorry for Jo.

Jack in the Box (R)

"Jack in the Box" jumps up like this
He makes me laugh as he waggles his head
I gently press him down again
Saying "Jack in the box' you must go to bed.

Smile Please (0)

Brush your teeth each morning
Brush your teeth at night
That's the way to keep them
Strong and shining white.

Eat a piece of apple
After having lunch
Better than a sweet to eat
It cleans teeth as you munch.

If you keep these simple rules
Everyone will say
"What lovely teeth you children hav
Let's see you smile today."

8

Jennie Muddlecombe (F)

Jennie Muddlecombe has lost her hat
She can't find it anywhere, well fancy that
She walked down the High Street and everyone said
"Funny old Jennie Muddlecombe, her hat is on her head.

The Red Light (D)

I ride my little bicycle,
I ride it to the shop
And when I see the big red light
I know that I must stop.

When I Grow Up

When I grow to be a man
I'll be a carpenter if I can
To saw, saw, saw the wood
Bang, bang, bang the nails
Oh what a lovely life.

When I grow to be a man
I'll be a soldier if I can
To march, march, march along
Beat, beat, beat the drum
Oh what a lovely life.

When I grow to be a man
I'll be a builder if I can
To pile, pile, pile the bricks
Splish, splash, splosh the paint
Oh what a lovely life.

When I grow to be a man
I'll be a gardener if I can
To dig, dig, dig the ground
Plant, plant, plant the seeds
Oh what a lovely life.

I'm a Soldier (E)

I'm a soldier straight and strong
See the way I march along.

I'm a postman rat-tat-tat
Dropping letters on your mat.

I'm a jockey on my horse
Jumping fences round the course.

I'm a policeman in the street
Walking up and down my beat.

I'm a coalman with a sack
See me drop it off my back.

I'm a painter with a ladder tall
See me painting all the wall.

I'm a gardener planting seeds
Digging, raking, pulling weeds.

I'm a batsman, playing cricket
See if you can hit my wicket.

I'm a swimmer in the sea
Splashing, diving, look at me!

What do I do? (M)

I am a window cleaner
What do I do?
Climb up my ladder
And I peep at you.

I am a policeman
What do I do?
Hold up the traffic
As the Queen drives through.

I am a bus conductor
What do I do?
Clip all the tickets
On the 202.

I am a postman
What do I do?
Post all the letters
And here's one for you.

9

Tommy's Penny Bun

Tommy bought a penny bun
From the baker's shop
Such a lovely shiny one
With sugar on the top
Along came a hungry dog
"Have a bit" said Tom
The dog liked it very much
And soon that bun was gone.

The Postman   (D)

Here comes the postman down the street
I hear the steady tramp of feet
I hear the click of the garden gate
And his steps on the path - just a moment to wa
Then slither and flop goes the mail on the mat
And he raps on the knocker, rat-a-tat-tat.

Sausage for tea   *(I Love a Lassie)*

I love a sausage, a bonny bonny sausage
I put one in the oven for my tea
I went down to the cellar
To get the salt and pepper
and the sausage ran after me.

Shopping   (H)

A little boy went walking
He walked into a store
He bought a pound of sausages
And laid them on the floor.
The boy began to whistle
He whistled up a tune
And all the little sausages
Danced around the room.

Goodnight   (D)

Ten little fingers
Ten little toes
Two little ears
And one little nose.
Two little eyes that shine so brig
One little mouth to kiss Mummy
                    "Goodnight."

Teapot   (S)

I'm a little teapot, short and stout
Here's my handle, here's my spout *(one hand
        on hip, other held out)*
When I get the steam up, hear me shout
Tip me up and pour me out.

Golliwog   (F)

Funny Mr. Golliwog goes tumbling along
With his face so black and his hair so long
Tumbling along - tumbling along
Funny Mr. Golliwog goes tumbling along.

Early in the Morning (S)

Down at the station early in the morning
See the little puffer trains all in a row
Man at the engine pulls a little lever
Ch-Ch. puff-puff, off we go.

Down at the harbour, early in the morning
See the little submarines all in a row
Man at the engine pull a little lever
Bubble, bubble, bubble, bubble, down we go.

Down at the airport, early in the morning
See the little aeroplanes all in a row
Pilot at the engine pulls a little joystick
Oo-oo-oo-oo, up we go.

Tea-time (I)

Tea time, tea time, come and have your tea
Bread and butter, cakes and jam for me,
I've had my bread and butter, I've drunk my cup of tea
What is there for supper?   Wait and see.

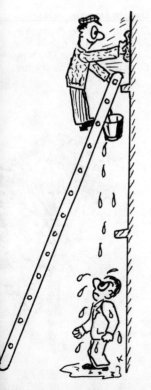

Window Cleaning

Click goes the ladder and the window cleaner man
Runs to the top as fast as he can.
He polishes the windows to make them shine,
And runs down again in double quick time.

Before You Cross the Road
(Tune 3 Blind Mice)

Stop look think
Stop look think
Before you cross the road
Before you cross the road
You use your eyes
You use your ears
You use your eyes and
You use your ears
And if no bus or car appears
Well then you cross the road
Well then you cross the road.

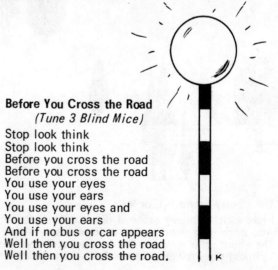

11

The Tree (B)

Here is the tree with its leaves so green	*(Arms stretched out)*
Here are the apples that hang between	*(Fists clenched)*
When the wind blows the apples fall	*(Fists falling from waving arms)*
Here is the basket to gather them all.	*(Make a basket with the hands).*

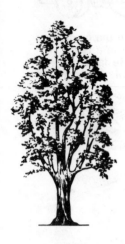

O Christmas Tree *(The Red Flag)*

O Christmas Tree, O Christmas Tree,
O what a lovely Christmas Tree.
Our Christmas Tree is tall and green
Our Christmas Tree is tall and green.

O Christmas Tree, O Christmas Tree,
O what a lovely Christmas Tree.
Our Christmas Tree is gay and bright
Our Christmas Tree is gay and bright.

O Christmas Tree, O Christmas Tree,
O what a lovely Christmas Tree.

We are lovely Chestnut Trees (D)

We are lovely chestnut trees,
Leaves are shaking in the breeze.
See us stand so straight and high
Looking upwards to the sky.
Wave our branches to and fro
Then make shade for flowers below.

Dingle Dangle (N)

Dingle Dangle deary me
Apples on the apple tree
Falling down on Dorothy
Dingle Dangle deary me.

The Cherry Stone (L or M)

I had a little cherry stone, I put it in the ground
And when next year I came to look, a tiny shoot I found
The shoot grew upwards day by day, and soon became a tree.
I picked the rosy cherries and ate them for my tea.

The Mouse (C)

A little mouse hid in a hole
Hid softly in a little hole
When all was quiet as quiet could be
Out popped he.

Wheels (D)

One wheel on a barrow,
Painted red and blue
Two wheels on my scooter
And on my cycle too.
Three wheels on a tricycle
But that's too small for me.
Four wheels on a motor car,
As any one can see.

Two Red Engines (A)

Two red engines standing in a row
With the carriages behind them
Waiting to go.
The engine driver takes his place,
The people all jump in,
The guard blows his whistle
And then the fun begins.
Chuff, chuff, chuffetty, chuff.

Is

-r-r" says the door bell when visitors call
-br" says the telephone bell in the hall
ng" says the bell on the big London bus
lang" says the fire engine "Make way for us"
ng" says the station bell "train won't be long"
t the bell in the steeple says "Dong, dong, dong".

I Can (A)

I can tie my shoe lace
I can brush my hair
I can wash my hands and face
And dry myself with care.
I can clean my teeth too
Fasten up my frocks
I can say "How do you do"
And pull up both my socks.

The Scarecrow (S)

When all the cows are sleeping
And the sun has gone to bed
Up jumped the scarecrow and this is what he said
I'm a dingly dangly scarecrow with a flippy floppy hat
I can shake my hands like this and shake my head like that.

13

Thumbkin (S)

Thumbkin he can dance
Thumbkin he can dance
We all go merrily up together
We all clap hands.

Pointer he can dance . . . . . .

Longman he can dance . . . . .

Ringman he can't dance
Ringman he can't dance
We can't go merrily up together
We can't clap hands.

Baby he can dance . . . .

Pointer Longman

Where is Thumbkin (K)

Where is thumbkin?   Where is thumbkin?
"Here I am.   Here I am".
"How are you this morning?"
"Very well I thank you."
"Say Goodbye.   Say Goodbye."

Continue with all the other fingers:

Peter Pointer, Tommy Tall, Ruby Ring & Baby Small.

Thumbkin

Tom Thumb (S)

Tommy Thumb

Here I am, he
Peter Pointer
Johnny Long
Ruby Ring . .
Baby Small .
Fingers all, f
Here we are,

How Do You Do

Two fat gentlemen met in a lane *(thumbs)*
Bowed most politely, bowed once again. *(thumbs bow to
                                   each other)*
"How do you do.   How do you do.   How do you do again".

Continue with all the other fingers: Two thin ladies,

two fat policemen, two big schoolboys, and two small babies.

These hands (I)

These hands are happy *(make fingers dance)*
These hands are sad   *(hang loosely)*
These hands are low   *(hang near ground)*
These hands are high   *(stretch up)*
These hands are going on a journey so wave good-bye *(good-*

The Family (B)

Here is the father short and stout *(thumb)*
Here is the mother with children all about *(1st finger)*
Here is a brother, tall as you see *(2nd finger)*
Here is the sister with dolly on her knee *(3rd finger and ring)*
Here is the baby still to grow *(little finger)*
Here is the family all in a row.

Bedtime (C)

This little girl is ready for bed *(right forefinger)*
On her pillow she lays her head *(put finger on left hand)*
Wraps herself in her blanket tight *(left fingers close over)*
Closes her eyes and says "Goodnight".

Morning comes, she opens her eyes
Back with a toss the blanket flies *(left fingers open)*
Up she gets, dresses and away
Down to the Nursery School to play.

an Baby

My Lady's . . . . . (C)

These are my lady's knives and forks
 (fingers interwoven, back of hands together)
Here is my Lady's table
 (fingers hidden, hands flat)
Here is my lady's looking glass
 (forefingers raised and joined)
And here is baby's cradle
 (little fingers also raised).

umb, where are you
                (thumb hidden)
w do you do *(thumb appears)*
. . etc.   *(first finger)*
.. etc.   *(second finger)*
. . etc.   *(third finger)*
. . etc.   *(fourth finger)*
where are you
, how do you do.

Fingers (D)

Open your fingers
Now shut them tight
Tuck them away till
They're out of sight.

Open your fingers
Now let them clap
Hold them up high
Then down in your lap.

Fling up your fingers
To reach the sky.
Flutter them down
And there let them lie.

lands

pen them, shut them, open them, shut them
        Give a little clap.
pen them, shut them open them, shut them
        Put them on your lap.
oll them, roll them, roll them, roll them,
        Roll them up like this.
ave them, wave them, wave them, wave them
        Blow a little kiss.
reep them, creep them, creep them, creep them
        Up to your little chin.
        Open wide your little mouth,
        And pop one finger in.

15

Movement Rhymes (B)

Small and round,
Small and round,
The bulb is deep
Inside the ground.

Stretch and grow,
Stretch and grow,
Up the stalk comes
Slow, slow slow.

The buds unfurl
The buds unfurl,
See the petals
Outward curl.

Straight and tall,
Straight and tall,
The flowers grow
Against the wall.

Walk very slowly
With great big stride.
Walk to a corner
Your head to hide.

Walk very quickly,
With steps very short.
Walk to a corner
And don't get caught.

Walk on your toes,
Now walk on your heels.
Then round go your legs
Like two engine wheels.

Tap your Head (D)

Tap your head,
And touch your toes.
Curl yourself up
Like a garden hose.
Stretch on the ground
Like a wheelbarrow wide.
Stand up straight
With your hands to your sides.

Two Little Hands Go Clap, Clap, Clap (A)

Two little hands go clap, clap, clap.
Two little feet go tap, tap, tap.
Two little arms go thump, thump, thump.
Two little feet go jump, jump, jump.
All the little children turn around.
All the little children sit on the ground.

Clap Hands (S)

We all clap hands together
We all clap hands together
We all clap hands together
And have a lovely time.

We all stand up together, etc.
We all sit down together, etc.
Jump up and down together, etc.
We all go to sleep together, etc.

Two Little Feet

Two little feet go tap tap tap
Two little hands go clap clap clap
Two little eyes are open wide
One head wags from side to side.

I Can Hear

I can hear my hands go *(clap, clap, clap)*
I can hear my feet go   *(tap, tap, tap)*
I can hear my mouth go *(click, click, click)*
But I can't hear my head go *(nod, nod, nod)*.

Let's all Jump Together (S)

Let's all jump together, jump together
Let's all jump together, jump, jump, jump,
Jump, jump, this away, jump, jump, that away.
Jump, jump, jump.

Let's all clap together . . . .

Let's all hop together . . . .

Let's all sing together . . . .

Tra la la

Big Brown Boots (F)

Big brown boots go
Tramp, tramp, tramp.
Little red shoes go
Stamp, stamp, stamp.
Silver slippers go
Trip, trip, trip.
And my two feet go
Skip, skip, skip.

Washing Day (C)

I went to visit a friend one day
She only lived across the way
She said she couldn't come out to play
Because it was her . . . (washing) . . . day

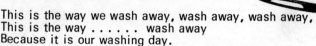

This is the way we wash away, wash away, wash away,
This is the way . . . . . . wash away
Because it is our washing day.

Ironing; Sweeping; Sewing; Polishing; Scrubbing, etc.

dy Bear (D)

dy Bear, Teddy Bear, dance on your toes
dy Bear, Teddy Bear, touch your nose
" " " " stand on your head
" " " " go to bed
" " " " wake up now
" " " " make your bow.

With my Hands (Polka Tune)

With my hands I clap clap clap
With my feet I tap tap tap
Right foot first, left foot next,
Round the world and back again.

With my eyes I see see see
With my ears I hear hear hear
Right foot first, left foot next,
Round the world and back again.

With my nose I smell smell smell
With my mouth I talk talk talk
Right foot first, left foot next,
Round the world and back again.

Peter (Trad.)

1. Peter works with one hammer, one hammer, one hammer
   (one fist)
   Peter works with one hammer, this fine day.
2. Peter works with two hammers . . . . (two fists)
3. Peter works with three hammers . . . (2 fists, 1 foot)
4. Peter works with four hammers . . . . (2 fists, 2 feet)
5. Peter works with five hammers . . . . (2 fists, 2 feet,
   head nodding)
6. Peter's very tired now.
7. Peter's going to sleep now.
8. Peter's waking up again.

We have these (G)

Fingers, thumbs and toes, eyes and ears and nose
Lips and chin, hair and skin,
Do you have all those?
Fingers, thumbs and toes, eyes and ears and nose,
Yes, we have all those,
Yes, we have all those.

Pancakes

Mix a pancake, stir a pancake
Pop it in the pan
Fry a pancake, toss a pancake
Catch it if you can.

My House

I'm going to build a little house, with a chimney tall
(arm in air)
A sloping roof and a garden wall *(hands draw roof &
wall)*
A big front door you can open wide
And two tiny windows you can peep inside. *(rings
with finger and thumb)*
I'm going to build a little table big enough for two
Two little chairs, one for me, one for you,
Knock at the knocker, and please come in
For my little house is shining like a bright new pin.
(open hands wide)

The House   (E)

Here is the house, the roof goes on *(draw the shape in
Two little chimneys all in a row   air)*
Clouds of smoke from the chimney go
Squiggle, squiggle, squiggle, so, so, so
One round window, two, three, four
and right in the middle is the little green door.

Build a House (E)

Build a house up, build it high
Point the chimney to the sky
Put the roof on, lay the floor
Paint the little yellow door
Here the mother bakes her bread
Here the baby goes to bed
Here the little children play
Dancing through the happy day.

Five Sticky Buns   (S)

Five sticky buns in a baker's shop
Big and brown with a currant on top.
A boy came along with a penny to pay
He paid one penny and he took a bun away.

Now there's four sticky buns in a baker's shop
   (etc. repeat 3, 2, 1)

No sticky buns in a baker's shop
Big and brown with a currant on top.
A boy came along with a penny to pay
"Sorry" said the baker "We have no buns left
                             today."

One, Two . . . .

One, two, something to do
Painting a picture and making it blue
Three, four, blocks on the floor
Building a tunnel as far as the door.
Five, six, toffee on sticks
Lemon and sugar and butter to mix.
Seven, eight, Dad at the gate
He must be early, or I must be late.
Nine, ten, I wonder when
I will be able to write with a pen.

Build a Snowman   (I)

We can build a snowman
We can make him high
We can build a snowman
Reaching for the sky.

We can build two snowmen
We can make them high
We can build two snowmen
Reaching for the sky.

We can build three   (etc. up to five)

Ten Little Gentlemen   (D)

Ten little gentlemen standing in a row
Bow little gentlemen bow down low.
Walk little gentlemen right across the floor.
And don't forget gentlemen, to please close
                             the door.

Raindrops (B)

Raindrops, raindrops, falling from the sky
Watering the garden when the ground is dry
Making little seeds grow into flowers tall
Hollyhocks will peep above the highest garden wall.

Rain *(Waltz Time)*

Down comes the rain.
Down comes the rain.
Beating on the roof
And on the window pane.
Flooding the gutter
And washing the street
With splishy splashy puddles
About my feet.
Dark are the clouds
Splash! It comes again
I'm as happy as a duckling
Paddling in the rain.

Marching in our Wellingtons (F

Marching in our Wellingtons
Tramp, tramp, tramp.
Marching in our Wellingtons
We won't get damp.
Splashing through the puddles
In the rain, rain, rain.
Splashing through the puddles
And splashing home again.

I hear Thunder (S)

I hear thunder
I hear thunder
Hark don't you
Hark don't you
Pitter patter raindrops
Pitter patter raindrops
I'm wet through
So are you

I see blue skies
I see blue skies
Way up high
Way up high
Hurry up the sunshine
Hurry up the sunshine
I'll soon dry
So will you.

It's raining

Please open your umbrella
Please open your umbrella
Please open your umbrella
To shield us from the rain.

The rain is nearly over
The rain is nearly over
The rain is nearly over
Then close it up again.

Snow *(Waltz Time)*

Softly softly falling so
This is how the snow flakes go
Softly softly falling so
Pitter-patter pitter pat.

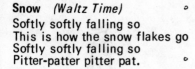

Jack Frost (J)

Look out, look out
Jack Frost is about
He's after your fingers and toes
And all through the night
The gay little sprite
Is working where nobody knows.

He climbs each tree
So nimble is he
His silvery powder he shakes
Across the grass he'll merrily pass
And turn all its greenness to white
Then home he will go
And laugh Ho-ho-ho-ho
What fun I have had in the night.

Wind

When the wind blows trees are bent low
And leaves fly about like the birds.
You cannot see wind or yet feel its shape
But you can, sometimes see where it's been.

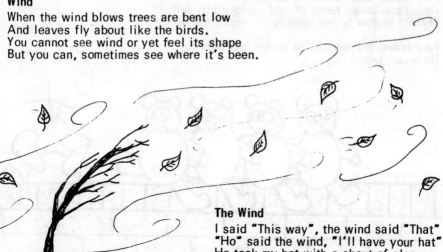

The Wind

I said "This way", the wind said "That"
"Ho" said the wind, "I'll have your hat"
He took my hat with a shout of glee
And hung it high on the top of a tree.

21

5 Little Soldiers (D)

5 little soldiers standing in a row,
4 stood straight and one stood so
(4 fingers standing straight & the thumb across them)
Along came the captain
And what do you think
Up jumped the soldiers quick as a wink.
(All fingers & thumb jumped up straight)

5 Brown Teddies (I)

Five brown teddies sitting on the wall
Five brown teddies sitting on the wall
And if one brown teddy should accidentally fall,
There'd be four brown teddies sitting on the wall.

Four brown teddies sitting on the wall,*etc. to*
No brown teddy . . . .

5 Little Lollipops (D)

Five little lollipops
Fixed upon a stick
Shall we have a taste of one?
Lick, lick, lick.

Four little lollipops
Fixed upon a stick, etc.

Five Little Squirrels (A)

Five little squirrels sitting in a tree
The first one said "What do I see?"
The second one said "A man with a gun"
The third one said "Let's run, let's run"
The fourth one said "Let's hide in the shade"
The fifth one said "I'm not afraid"
BANG went the gun, and away they all ran.

Ten Little Men

Ten little men standing straight
Ten little men open the gate
Ten little men in a ring
Ten little men bow to the King
Ten little men dance all day
Ten little men hide away.

Rosy Apples (A)

5 rosy apples by the cottage door
One tumbled off the twig, then there were 4.

4 rosy apples hanging on the tree
The farmer's wife took one, and then there were 3.

3 rosy apples, what shall I do?
I think I'll have one, then there'll be 2.

2 rosy apples hanging in the sun,
You have the big one, that will leave 1.

1 rosy apple, soon it is gone;
The wind blew it off the branch,
Now there is none !

23

Ten Chickens   (B)

Two little chickens looking for some more
Along came another two and they make four.

Four little chickens getting in a fix
Along came another two and they make six.

Six little chickens perching on a gate
Along came another two and they make eight.

Eight little chickens run to Mother Hen
Along came another two and they make ten.

Five Little Peas   (D)

Five little peas in a peapod pressed
One grew, two grew, and so did all the rest.
They grew and grew and never stopped,
Until at last that peapod popped.

Fat Sausages   (D)

Five fat sausages frying in a p
All of a sudden one went "ban
Four fat sausages . . . . e
Three fat sausages . . . . . . e

The Swimming Fishes

Five little fishes swimming in a pool
This one says the pool is cool
This one says the pool is deep
This one says I'd like to sleep
This one says I'd float and dip
This one says I see a ship.
Fisherman's boat comes
The line goes splash.

With My Little . . . (M)

With my little brush I sweep sweep sweep
With my little hand I creep creep creep
With my little eyes I peep peep peep
On my little bed I sleep sleep sleep.

Flying Saucers (S)

Five little men in a flying saucer
Flew round the world one day.
They looked from left to right of it
Could not stand the sight of it, so one man flew away.

Four little men etc.   Three - Two - One.

The Snowman (A)

A Snowman stood on snowy ground
Five little children dancing round
One fell down with a bump
How many left to dance about.   FOUR

A Snowman stood on snowy ground
Four little children dancing round. etc.

Three - Two - One.

A Snowman stood on snowy ground
One little child dancing round
She fell down with a bump
How many left to dance about.   NONE

A Snowman stood on snowy ground
No little children dancing round
Then up they jumped with a shout
"Here we are to dance about."

Five Little Monkeys   (A)

Five little monkeys playing by the shore
One went sailing, then there were four.
Four little monkeys climbed up a tree,
One climbed too high, then there were three.
Three little monkeys playing in the glue,
One got stuck in it, then there were two.
Two little monkeys had a currant bun,
One ran away with it, then there was one.
One little monkey cried all afternoon,
So they put him in an aeroplane and sent him to the moon.
No more little monkeys playing on the shore,
That's the end of my song
And now there is no more.

Ten Little Soldiers   (D)

Ten little soldiers standing in a row
They all bow down to their Captain so
They march to the left
They march to the right
They march straight home
And sleep all night.

Little Ducks   (S)

Five little ducks went out one day
Over the hills and far away.
Mother duck said "quack, quack, quack, quack"
And four little ducks came swimming back.

Four little ducks . . . .
    (repeat with 3, 2, 1)

Mother duck went out one day
Over the hills and far away.
Mother duck said "quack, quack, quack, quack"
And five little ducks came swimming back.

K.

One Red Engine

One Red Engine chuffing down the track
One Red Engine chuffing, chuffing, back.

Two Red Engines chuffing down the track
etc. . . . .

Eight Big Fingers   (B)

Eight big fingers standing up tall
Two little ears to hear Mummy call
One little nose that I can blow
Ten little toes all in a row.
Two short thumbs that wriggle up and down
Two little feet to stand on the ground
Hands to clap and eyes to see
Oh what fun to be just me.

10 Fat Policemen

10 fat Policemen stand up straight *(fingers up)*
10 fat Policemen make a gate   *(fingers interlock)*
10 fat Policemen bow to the Queen *(bend fingers)*
10 fat Policemen make a ring   *(finger tips together)*
10 fat Policemen parade all day   *(make fingers walk)*
10 fat Policemen hide again   *(hands behind back)*

KRIS.

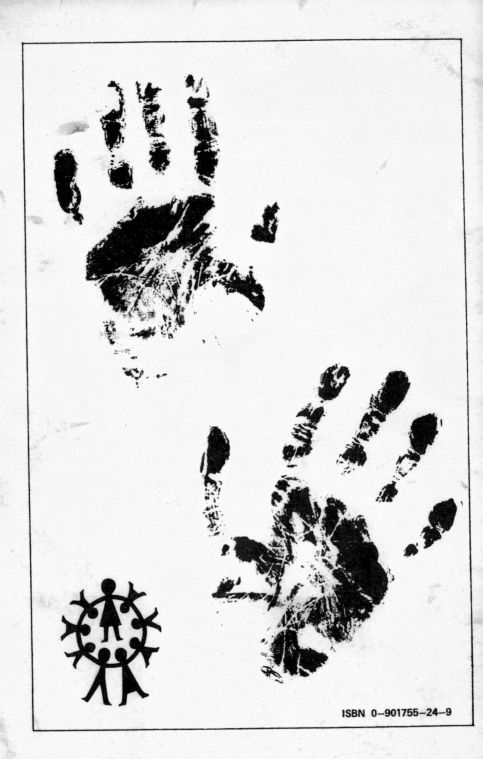

ISBN 0—901755—24—9

DEDICATED

To the Crew of Daisy II

THE reason why I am paying a special dedication to the late crew of the Daisy II with whom I served on the fateful night at Scapa Flow, is that I am now the only one alive in the crew left to fulfil their wishes that their story should be told.

More than 800 brave men lost their lives that fateful morning of Saturday, 14th October, 1939, when the Battleship HMS Royal Oak was torpedoed and sunk in what had been thought to be an impregnable anchorage.

I never thought I would meet men of such courage in time of peril on the sea. They had great faith and that's what kept us going; our strength that night was beyond human endurance. They gave their all, and asked for nothing back.

I remember clearly, even although more than half-a-century has passed, we all worked together that night as a team, picking men out of the water, with our strength growing weaker all the time, but the Divine Spirit was with us.

Our skipper, John Gatt DSC, was a man of great faith in his God, and kept his great courage all through that night; that helped the rescue greatly - but as the long dawn came, there was a deadly silence in Scapa Flow, because over 800 men were still missing, and had no more chance of survival.

By the time dawn broke, we were now, just six men confused and tired, but amidst the sorrow that so many brave sailors had lost their lives, we had the joy of knowing that we had rescued 360 men from a watery grave.

1